Greetings
Operation Bookshelf
Scarsdale Woman's Club
Scarsdale, N. Y., U. S. A. 10583

INTERNATIONAL SERIES OF MONOGRAPHS ON
ELECTRONICS AND INSTRUMENTATION

GENERAL EDITORS: D. W. FRY and W. HIGINBOTHAM

VOLUME 18

OTHER TITLES PUBLISHED IN THE SERIES

(FORMERLY PERGAMON SCIENCE SERIES ELECTRONICS AND WAVES)

PROBLEMS IN THE DESIGN AND DEVELOPMENT OF 750 MW TURBOGENERATORS

Problems in the Design and Development of 750 MW Turbogenerators

by

V. P. ANEMPODISTOV,
E G. KASHARSKII and I. D. URUSOV

Translated by
O. M. BLUNN

Technical adviser for the English translation
V. EASTON
G.E.C. BIRMINGHAM

A Pergamon Press Book

THE MACMILLAN COMPANY
NEW YORK
1963

THE MACMILLAN COMPANY
60 Fifth Avenue
New York 11, N.Y.

This book is distributed by
THE MACMILLAN COMPANY, NEW YORK
pursuant to a special arrangement with
PERGAMON PRESS LIMITED
Oxford, England.

Copyright © 1963
Pergamon Press Ltd.

This translation has been made from a book by V. P. Anempodistov, E. G. Kasharskii and I. D. Urusov entitled *Problemy krupnogo turbo-generatorostroyeniya* published in Moscow–Leningrad 1960 by the Academy of Sciences of the U.S.S.R.

Library of Congress Card Number 63-11925

Printed by The Compton Printing Works (London) Ltd.

Made in England

CONTENTS

PREFACE

The purpose of this book is to draw the attention of engineers, metallurgists and scientists to problems in the development of very large turbo-generators. The selected problems mainly relate to projected machines and hence the authors have often had to rely on research and design studies. But this should not detract from the value of a book which does not set out to make practical recommendations, but only to throw light on main trends in design and point the way to further research and development.

The book describes the main lines of research at the Electromechanics Institute of the U.S.S.R. Academy of Sciences under the direction of academician M. P. Kostenko in co-operation with the electrical industry.

Sections I and II have been written by V. P. Anempodistov, section III by E. G. Kasharskii, sections V and VI by I. D. Urusov whilst in section IV all the authors have collaborated.

The authors wish to acknowledge their gratitude to N. V. Bartan'yan who performed many of the calculations used in this book.

The authors

CHAPTER I

INTRODUCTION

The rapid economic development of the U.S.S.R. requires equally rapid progress in the generation of electricity, now the main factor in technical progress. Table 1 shows the output of electricity in the U.S.S.R. since 1945 and the planned increase for 1965.

TABLE 1

Years	Output milliard kW.hr
1945	43.3
1950	91.2
1955	170.1
1958	233
1965 (planned)	500 – 520

The present plans to increase the generation of electricity are primarily based on new coal-burning power stations which require much less capital outlay than hydro-electric stations. Capital investment and operating costs can also be reduced by building larger power stations and producing larger single units. The coal-burning power stations which are now under construction have been designed with this saving in mind and it is planned to instal sets of 200 and 300 MW output and even larger units. This increase in unit power corresponds to a scale of output from the various power systems which is limited by the regulations governing power system stand-by arrangements (power reserves). Both in the U.S.S.R. and the U.S.A., this maximum is considered to be

1

of the order of 5 to 7 per cent of the installed power of the system [6].

According to published estimates [1], the U.S.S.R. must produce 1000 to 1200 milliard kW.hr/annum by 1970 to 1975. To ensure this output of energy, the installed capacity of the U.S.S.R. power system must reach 250-300 million kW. This requires the development of very large turbo-generators.

The interconnection of the individual power systems of the U.S.S.R. in a single national grid will remove the limitations imposed on unit output by operating conditions and therefore the maximum output of future units will depend solely on engineering and economic factors.

The graph in Fig. 1 illustrates the annual increase in unit output of turbo-generators since 1920. To maintain the same rate of increase up to 1975-1978, the maximum power of turbo-generators must reach 750-1000 MW.

This trend towards increased unit output both in the U.S.S.R. and abroad is due firstly to demands for rapid increases in the installed power of coal-burning power stations and secondly to the considerable savings to be achieved by increasing the power of single units. Research by foreign and Soviet specialists [1, 2] shows that power station fuel costs are directly related to steam temperature and pressure. Improvements in steam utilization allow a considerable reduction in specific fuel consumption and reduce total power station costs. It is necessary to bear in mind that each range of steam pressures and temperatures has a corresponding optimum unit-output at which the energy of the steam is utilized most economically. In order to judge the saving due to increases in unit output and improved steam utilization, Fig. 2 shows curves which relate the cost of installed power and specific fuel consumption to unit size.

According to the available data in the foreign and Soviet press [1, 2, 3, 4, 5], in the next 15 to 20 years it will be possible to increase steam temperature to $700-750°C$ and steam pressure to $400-500$ atm, which will almost halve the specific fuel consumption compared with what it is today. However, it is essential to have single units of corresponding power in

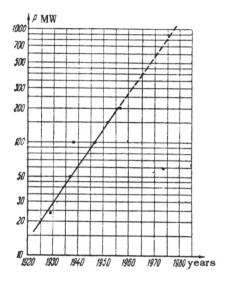

FIG. 1. Annual rate of
increase in unit size
of turbo-generators.

order to realize these reductions in practice. Outputs of the
order of 600 to 750 MW are required. Now is the time to consider the feasibility of such units. The generator and turbine are
the most important parts.

There is already a projected 320 MW electrical generator and
single-shaft turbine in the U.S.S.R. and one of 325 MW in the
U.S.A. (Westinghouse). Judging from the results of these pro-
jects, it is practicable and economically expedient to increase
still further the output of single-shaft turbo-generators.

This book presents a synopsis of the main problems in the
development of such plant and points a way to their solution

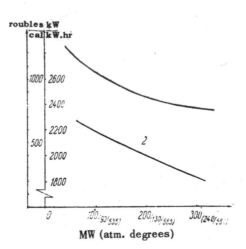

FIG. 2. The main economic indices
of coal-burning power stations in relation to unit output and steam utilization:
1 — cost per kW installed;
2 — specific fuel consumption per
    kW.hr.

from the results of research at the Electromechanics Institute
of the U.S.S.R. Academy of Sciences and other scientific and
industrial organisations.

Reference should be made to the glossary of notation as
required.

In the English translation the Electromechanics Institute
of the U.S.S.R. Academy of Sciences is referred to simply as the
Electromechanics Institute. It is not however to be confused
with the All-Union Electromechanics Research Institute.

CHAPTER II

DIRECT COOLING
AND MAXIMUM OUTPUT

The output of an electrical machine can be increased without changing the dimensions of its active parts by increasing the specific loading of the rotor and stator and permitting a greater current density in the windings. To increase the unit power of a turbo-generator, it is therefore necessary to provide a more efficient cooling system, especially for the windings.

The problem has been successfully solved by direct cooling of the winding copper. This has increased the utilization of active materials by a factor of 2 to 2.5 whereas forced cooling, when the cooling surface is increased by additional ducts in the core and greater hydrogen pressures are used in the casing, only results in an improvement of 10 to 15 per cent. In conventional cooling systems the loss in the winding copper is mainly dissipated from the surface of the steel cores containing the windings. The heat flow has to overcome several thermal resistances, and the sum of the temperature-drops in these resistances is equal to the temperature rise of the windings [7]. The following resistances and temperature drops are involved: 1, that in the winding insulation; 2, in the steel lamination; 3, at the cooling surface and 4, in the gas.

The distribution of the temperature gradients relating to the copper of a conventionally cooled rotor is illustrated in Fig. 3 for various gas pressures.

It will be seen from this diagram that the main components of the temperature rise are the drops in the insulation and steel. Only the latter drop can be reduced by additional ventilation ducts. An increase in gas pressure reduces the drops at the

surface and in the gas, but those in the insulation and steel
remain unchanged. Both methods of improving forced cooling,
decrease the overall temperature rise or allow an increase in
output, but the latter involves a higher heat drop in the winding insulation. There is a definite limit to this heat drop in

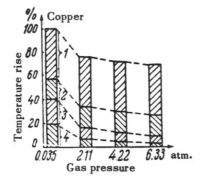

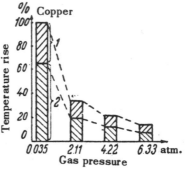

FIG. 3. The distribution of the
temperature rise over the zones
of thermal resistance for the rotor
windings with conventional
hydrogen cooling:
1 — drop in the insulation;
2 — drop in the steel;
3 — drop at the cooling surface;
4 — temperature rise of cooling
   gas.

FIG. 4. The distribution of the
temperature rise over the zones
of thermal resistance for the
rotor windings with direct
hydrogen cooling.
1 — drop at the cooling surface;
2 — temperature rise of the cooling gas.

the insulation which is set by its reliability and therefore a
corresponding limit to increases in output by more intensive
surface cooling of the windings.

In direct cooling, the cooling medium is driven along ducts
in the winding copper and the major drops in the insulation and
steel are eliminated; the temperature rise of the copper has only
two components (see Fig. 4) and the total rise depends solely
on the type of cooling medium and its rate of flow through the
ducts.

Table 2 shows the heat transfer capacity of various cooling

TABLE 2

Cooling medium	Relative density	Relative volume	Relative heat transfer capacity
Air	1	1	1
Hydrogen (0.035 atm)	0.138	1	0.75
Hydrogen (2.1 atm)	0.21	1	3.0
Transformer oil	848	0.012	21.0
Water.	1000	0.012	50

media at normal rates of flow.

It will be seen from this Table that the most efficient system is water cooling. This is now widely used for the stators of large turbo-generators. Calculations also show that water cooling is the most economical owing to the possibility of smaller internal ducts in the winding copper. The dissipated heat can also be used for boiler feed water heating.

Owing to the design and production difficulties associated with water cooling at the high rotational speeds of modern turbogenerators, the rotor winding is cooled by hydrogen at high pressures of 3 to 4 atm. With direct hydrogen-cooled rotor windings it has been possible to produce 325 MW generators which are no larger in size than earlier machines of much lower power. Further improvement in the utilization of active materials entails increasing overall dimensions or using liquid cooling for the rotor as well as the stator. Much research is now being carried out in other countries besides the U.S.S.R. to design and produce reliable water-cooled rotors.

The use of internal ducts has altered the design of the windings and other constructional parts have been changed by the different system of cooling. Very many different designs have been put forward by factories in the U.S.S.R. and abroad, especially for the internal ducts of water-cooled rotor windings [7]. Design engineers in some factories have tried to avoid apertures

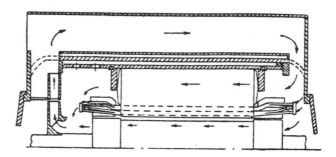

FIG. 5. Axial system of cooling with one-way flow of cooling gas
(Allis Chalmers)

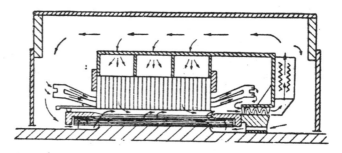

FIG. 6. Axial system of cooling with two-way flow of cooling gas
(Westinghouse)

in the slot insulation; this can be achieved by blowing the cooling gas along axial channels which must extend beyond the active length of the rotor. This type of cooling system is illustrated in Fig. 5.

However, this axial system of cooling with a one-way flow of cooling gas has a number of real disadvantages. In the first place, the temperature is unevenly distributed axially along the machine which notably reduces the effect of direct cooling since the permissible specific loading (the output of the machine)

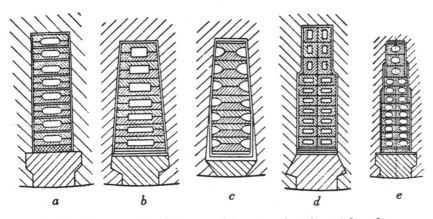

FIG. 7. Cross-sectional shapes of the rotor slots for axial cooling
system.

a — Kharkov Electrical Engineering Works, U.S.S.R.;
b — Westinghouse;
c — Allis Chalmers;
d — G.E.C.;
e — Brown-Boveri.

is limited, not by the mean temperature over its length, but by
the maximum local temperature. Secondly, if the length of the
machine is considerable, the drop in gas pressure in the ducts
is so great that the required pressure head becomes a serious
problem.

The two-way axial system of cooling shown in Fig. 6 is a
superior method as regards both the pressure drop in the winding
ducts and the temperature distribution along the machine. The
presence of outlet apertures in the middle of the body does not
affect the production of the rotor or its operation.

The internal ducts of axially-cooled rotor windings are
also very diverse in cross-sectional shape. Various systems are
shown in Fig. 7 [7, 8].

It is obvious that the best cooling for a given cross-sectional
area of duct and rate of flow obtains when the gas flows along
ducts in the conductors. However, in selecting the shape and

position of the ducts to suit the cross section of the slot, a considerable part is played by technological factors and the question of mechanical reliability. Technological considerations also determine the shape of the slot, i.e. whether it is to be rectangular or trapezoidal. The latter shape provides much better utilization of the slot zone of the rotor, but the method of production is complicated.

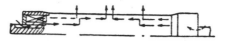

FIG. 8. Rotor cooling with divided flow of cooling gas.

It is a common disadvantage of all systems in which the gas flows axially, that the copper is unevenly heated over the length of the rotor. In individual cases, the local temperature may be twice the mean temperature and the effectiveness of direct cooling is considerably reduced.

Divided flow of incoming cooling gas (see Fig. 8) does not overcome this disadvantage and if many parallel paths are provided, considerable constructional difficulties arise. Axial cooling systems also require high pressure fans (compressors) which have a low operating efficiency and when used for turbo-generators their considerable power consumption (hundreds of kilowatts) markedly reduces the overall efficiency of the generator.

Use has been made of centrifugal (Fig. 5) and multi-stage (Fig. 6) axial compressors for turbo-generators. The advantage of centrifugal fans is their smaller axial dimensions, but they are more highly stressed mechanically and this limits their use.

Alternatively, a special separately mounted compressor may be used to circulate the gas but this necessitates additional gas ducts which complicates the cooling system and reduces the operating reliability of the set.

The axial system of rotor cooling has been developed and used by the same factories and companies (the Kharkov Electrical Engineering Works in the U.S.S.R., General Electric, Allis Chalmers and Westinghouse in the U.S.A.) which also used gas for cooling the stator windings. For stator windings a purely axial system is used to maintain intact the ground insulation of the conductor bars and this for gas cooling requires a high pressure compressor. A later development is the use of transformer oil or distilled water to cool the stator windings [9, 10, 11].

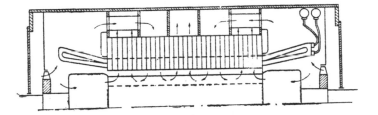

FIG. 9. Gap pickup

The use of liquid coolants for the stator and gas for the rotor required a rotor cooling-system which is equally efficient with conventional low-pressure fans. Two types of "gap pickup" rotor cooling-systems have since been developed (Fig. 9); one by the General Electric [7] and one by Elektrosila in the U.S.S.R. [12, 13].

Whereas in the normal axial system the duct inlets are in the overhang under the end bell, where the cooling gas is delivered from a compressor, in rotors with gap pickup the shorter axial ducts have inlet and outlet ports on the rotor surface. The latter is divided axially into a number of sections having alternately systems of inlet and outlet ports. In the slots the cooling ducts in the General Electric system are within the winding conductors (Fig. 10), but in the Soviet version produced by Elektrosila they are on the surface of the coils in the form of inclined ducts on the sides as shown in Fig. 11.

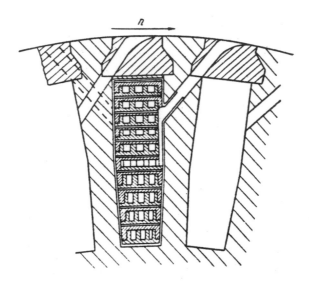

FIG. 10. Cross-section of rotor slot with gap pickup
(General Electric)

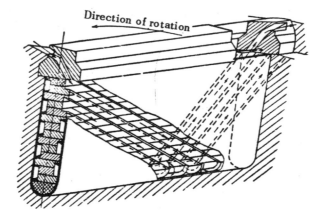

FIG. 11. Cross-section of rotor slot and shape of the
ducts for gap pickup
(Elektrosila, U. S. S. R.)

The gas is circulated in the rotor ducts by the pressure head which is developed due to rotation at the inlet ports which face the direction of rotation. The rate of flow depends on the cross sectional dimensions of the ducts, their configuration and the shape of the inlet ports. The number of sections with inlet and outlet ports is determined for each design by heat analysis and test data. The number of inlet and outlet zones usually corresponds to the number of hot and cold gas zones in the stator casing, since this matched system is more efficient. The length of each duct does not exceed 0.8m. The speed of the gas in the ducts with gap pickup is about 30 to 35 per cent of the actual speed of the rotor [13].

The advantage of gap pickup is the greater uniformity of cooling along the rotor length. An added advantage is that a high pressure fan is no longer required, conventional fans being adequate for the overall circulation of the gas. However, in order to judge the economic advantages of gap pickup compared with the axial system, it is necessary to determine the power consumption of the two systems under the same conditions. This answer will only be found by the tests and scientific investigations which are now in progress at factories and research organizations. One of the most important aspects of this problem is the optimum geometry of the internal ducts and inlet ports in gap pickup. Preliminary investigations have shown that there is scope for great saving in the cost of the gap-pickup system by careful study and subsequent improvement of the characteristics of the intakes on models and prototype equipment.

Both hydrogen and liquid coolants are still used for direct cooling of the stator windings, but water cooling has recently come to be used on a particularly large scale. This is the most effective and economical method. From test results at a number of organizations, distilled water possesses the most favourable properties and its dielectric strength is adequate for the direct cooling of windings at high voltages.

The disposition of the internal ducts in the stator conductors differs from design to design. For hydrogen cooling it is acknowledged (Kharkov Electrical Engineering works and Westinghouse) that the most rational position of the ventilation ducts is in the centre of the conductors over the full height (see Fig. 12, *a*). The cooling gas is supplied from a compressor at one end of the stator and discharged at the other end. In practice the ventilation ducts are formed by a number of thin-walled metal tubes between the stacks of copper laminations (Fig. 33), the tube material being non-magnetic and having a high specific resistance.

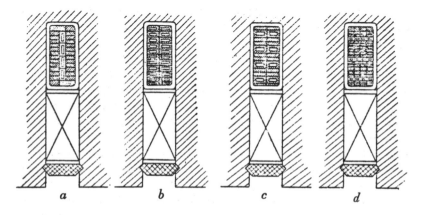

FIG. 12. Cross-section of the stator conductors with direct cooling. Explanation in the text.

For liquid cooling the cross sectional area of the individual ducts can be considerably reduced without risk of exceeding the permissible pressure drop over the conductor length. This has allowed the manufacture of stator bars from hollow subconductors (Fig. 12, *b*). The most efficient system of cooling is for cooling liquid to flow along ducts in each subconductor, but the presence of a duct makes it necessary to increase the thickness of the conductors which results in a considerable increase in the copper loss.

Use is now made of a combined system of hollow and solid conductors to reduce the additional loss (Fig. 12, *c*). Cooling efficiency is thereby reduced, but it is still quite high and a considerable increase in the specific loading of the stator is possible.

In large machines, in order to reduce the winding loss, it may be advisable to use thin-walled tubes of metal with a high specific resistance for liquid coolants, instead of the hollow copper subconductors. The tubes may be arranged as in Fig. 12 (a) or in horizontal rows (Fig. 12, d).

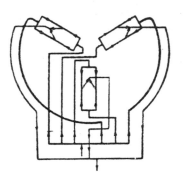

FIG. 13. Circulation of the cooling water in the stator winding (G.E.C.)

Owing to the high efficiency of water cooling, it becomes possible to connect two or more stator coils in series with correspondingly fewer water pipes which are complicated constructional units. For this purpose the G.E.C. has developed a system in which the cooling water passes successively through all the coils of each half-phase (Fig. 13).

The circulation of cooling liquid is generally arranged on a closed system in which the hot water is cooled in special heat exchangers by means of raw or distilled water before it is re-circulated through the machine. Open systems are also now being developed in which the condensate is used to cool the windings before entering the boiler.

Direct cooling of the windings does not eliminate the need to cool the stator core, which may have either a radial or axial system of ventilation with gas or liquid coolant. Usually, with gap pickup for the rotor, the core has radial ventilation (Elektrosila and General Electric), but if axial systems are employed for the rotor, then an axial gas (Allis Chalmers) or liquid (Brown-Boveri) system is employed for the core.

Much attention is now being paid to the large scale introduction of liquid cooling for the cores and special interest is attached to the development of oil-filled stators. This idea is not new [15], but it is only in large machines with direct copper cooling that this method has become of undoubted interest from the point of view of replacing mica products by inexpensive oil-resistant insulation.

These few remarks will help the reader to assess the relative value of the various direct cooling systems in turbo-generator design. Only the development of direct cooling has made possible the continuation of the present rate of progress in unit output. It will be shown in section IV that forced cooling is by no means the only way of increasing unit output.

But the expedient degree of material utilization naturally depends on such factors as rotor size, total cost and performance. These too must be considered.

CHAPTER III

A THEORETICAL ANALYSIS
OF "GEOMETRIC SERIES" OF LARGE
TURBO-GENERATORS

1. PRELIMINARY REMARKS

The specific power of modern two-pole turbo-generators* is greater than that of any other type of electrical machine, i.e. in output per unit of volume. Large specific loadings and high levels of mechanical utilization are therefore typical of turbo-generators.

The main mechanical factors limiting the dimensions of turbo-generators are as follows.

(a) The diameter of the rotor which is limited by the stresses in the body of the rotor and end bell due to centrifugal forces.

(b) The length of the rotor which is limited by the need to maintain a level of rigidity such that the normal speed of the rotor is usually between the first and second critical speeds.

Up to the present there has been no particular reason to increase the rotor length so as to run through the second critical speed. Calculations have shown that a ratio l_t/D_i greater than 4 to 5 gives no improvement in generator characteristics [16]. On the other hand even a small increase in rotor diameter with the ratio l_t/D_i practically optimum (3.5 to 4.5) will bring a substantial improvement. The possibility and expediency of increasing the rotor diameter therefore deserves special attention when considering increased unit output [35]. It should be

---

* Turbo-generators with a large number of poles are not used on a large scale at the present time.

pointed out that existing rotor diameters are about 1075 to
1150 mm and even a small increase (50 to 100 mm) involves the
solution of very complex scientific and technological problems.
The choice of rotor diameter for a particular generator therefore
entails a detailed analysis of the relationship between the
characteristics of the generator on the one hand and its diameter and power on the other.

In this section a general theoretical analysis is made of the
relationship between the main characteristics of a machine and
its power for "ideal geometric series" and "series with constant
diameter" in order to elucidate the prospects for further increases in rotor diameter.

2. THE VARIATION OF THE CHARACTERISTICS OF "IDEAL GEOMETRIC SERIES" AND "SERIES WITH CONSTANT DIAMETER" WITH INCREASING OUTPUT

The design of a series of electrical machines for specified
outputs is usually based on the relationship between their main
dimensions (diameter and active length) and their output. This
relationship provides the appropriate expressions for the electromagnetic loading and later for the reactances, losses, inertia
constants and so on.

In an overall analysis of a series of electrical machines use
is normally made of the general relationship for an "ideal geometric series", i.e. for a series in which the main dimensions
are proportional to the fourth root of the output. The assumption
of an ideal series presupposes the possibility of an unrestricted
increase in both the length l_t and diameter D_i without appreciable effect on the specific electromagnetic loading (current
density s and gap flux density B_δ). But this assumption only
applies (and even then only very approximately) to small and
medium machines up to 50 MW without direct cooling. Between
50 and 150 MW the length increases greatly with very small
increases in diameter*. Over 150 MW increases in output are

---

* The Soviet TV-2 type generators produced by Elektrosila are in mind.

achieved by forced cooling. The relationship of an "ideal geometric series" do not apply to generators of this class. The extreme case is a series with direct cooling with its main dimensions constant (except for the length of the gap). The basis of a series with constant frame size presupposes that the forced cooling of the generator can be improved indefinitely and that the temperature rise can be held within permissible limits with increasing output.

Table 3 shows the relationship between various generator characteristics and output P_a for the two types of series. It is assumed that the synchronous reactance x_d is maintained constant in both series by varying the gap length. The characteristics of the first series are generally known. Those of the second series show that an appreciable increase in copper loss, specific loading, current density and leakage reactance is associated with increasing output.

An increase in the quantities associated with the leakage flux of the stator and rotor causes the design to approach closer to its "maximum electromagnetic power". The "maximum electromagnetic power" for a given dimension will now be considered.

In a conventionally-cooled electrical machine, the power limit for a given dimension and S.C.R. usually depends on the maximum permissible thermal loading. But in electrical machines with direct cooling, it is in principle possible to dissipate very large losses without undue temperature rise. The amount of flux in the rotor teeth is usually limited by the saturation of the steel. The proportion of leakage flux to rotor flux increases continually with increasing power for a given constant size.

Putting Φ_1 for the flux determining the stator voltage, i.e. the stator flux on no load and at rated voltage, the stator flux on rated load is

$$\Phi_1' = \Phi_1 \cdot E'_v. \tag{1}$$

In relative units the internal e.m.f. E'_v is

$$E'_v = 1 + c_1 F_a, \tag{2}$$

TABLE 3

Characteristic	Symbol	Relationship with power	
		of an "ideal geometric series"	of a series with constant frame size
Diameter of rotor body	D_2, l_t	$\equiv \sqrt[4]{(P_a)}$	const
Gap	δ	$\equiv \sqrt[4]{(P_a)}$	$\equiv P_a$
Gap flux density*	B_δ	$\approx$ const	$\approx$ const
Specific loading of stator (rotor)	A_1, A_2	$\equiv \sqrt[4]{(P_a)}$	$\equiv P_a$
Current density	s	const	$\equiv P_a$
Main copper loss as a proportion of rated power	$Q'_{Cu(rel)}$	$\equiv 1/\sqrt[4]{(P_a)}$	$\equiv P_a$
The same for iron	$Q'_{Fe(rel)}$	$\equiv 1/\sqrt[4]{(P_a)}$	$\cong 1/P_a$
Leakage reactance of stator, p.u.	x_s	$\equiv \sqrt[4]{(P_a)}$	$\equiv P_a$
Inertia constant	H_j	$\equiv \sqrt[4]{(P_a)}$	$\equiv 1/P_a$
Excitation power, kW	Q_{ex}	$\equiv P_a^{3/4}$	$\equiv P_a^2$

where c_1 depends on the slot geometry and number of turns in the stator winding, and defines the slot leakage.

Under rated conditions the rotor flux is equal to the stator flux plus the leakage fluxes Φ_{0s} and Φ_{as} of the rotor,

$$\Phi_2 = \Phi'_1 + \Phi_{0s} + \Phi_{as}. \tag{3}$$

---

* In actual fact the flux density varies slightly in both series, but this variation is ignored in order to simplify the analysis.

The flux Φ_{os} corresponds to the rotor leakage due to the no load m.m.f. and Φ_{as} to that due to the armature reaction, i.e.

$$\Phi_{os} = \Phi_{sn\dot{o}} + \Phi_{s\delta,o} = c_2 F_0,$$

$$\Phi_{as} = \Phi_{snk} + \Phi_{s\delta k} = c_3 F_a.$$

Since if the S.C.R. is constant,

$$F_0 \approx c_4 F_a,$$

therefore,

$$\Phi_2 = \Phi'_1 + c_5 F_a$$

or

$$\Phi_2 = \Phi_1 + c F_a . \tag{4}$$

Machine power can of course be written in terms of F_a and Φ_1

$$P_a = k_p \Phi_1 F_a \tag{5}$$

Substituting the value of Φ_1 from (4),

$$P_a = k_p \left[\Phi_2 F_a - c F_a^2 \right]. \tag{6}$$

Equating the differential $\delta P_a / \delta F_a$ to zero and substituting in (6) the quantity $F_{a(max)}$, the maximum power is

$$P_{a\,(max)} = k_p \frac{\Phi_2^2}{4c}. \tag{7}$$

Formula 7 only provides a very rough estimate of maximum electromagnetic power since much depends on the individual features of a machine (dimensions of the active belt, the number of turns etc).

It will be seen that formula 7 is similar to that for the maximum torque of an induction motor.

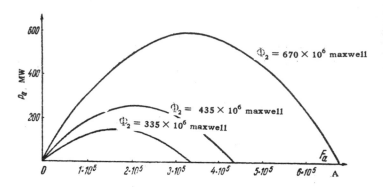

FIG. 14. Active power as a function of the armature reaction m.m.f. for a generator of given rotor diameter at various values of the permissible rotor flux (Φ_2).

Example. Suppose it is required to estimate the maximum electromagnetic power of a turbo generator under the following conditions:

$$D_2 = 1150 \text{ mm},$$
$$l_2 = 5500 \text{ mm},$$
$$\Phi_2 = \text{const} = 670 \times 10^6 \text{ maxwell},$$

if for $P = 300$ MW

$$F_a = 98700 \text{ A},$$
$$\Phi_1 = 569 \times 10^6 \text{ maxwell}.$$

Then, by definition,

$$k_P = \frac{P}{F_a \cdot \Phi_1} = \frac{300 \times 10^6}{98700 \cdot 569 \times 10^6} = 0.54 \times 10^{-5} \frac{\text{W}}{\text{maxwell} \cdot \text{A}},$$

$$c = \frac{\Phi_2 - \Phi_1}{F_a} = \frac{670 - 569}{98700} \times 10^6 = 10^3 \frac{\text{maxwell}}{\text{A}}.$$

The maximum electromagnetic power is therefore

$$P_{\text{lim.max}} = k_P \left[\frac{\Phi_2^2}{4c} \right] = 0.54 \times 10^{-5} \left[\frac{6.7^2 \times 10^{16}}{4 \times 10^3} \right] = 6 \times 10^8 \text{ W},$$

$$P_{\text{lim.max}} \approx 600 \text{ MW}.$$

Figure 14 shows the power for a given diameter as a function of the armature reaction m.m.f. F_a. The calculations were performed for three values of rotor flux: $\Phi_2 = 670 \times 10^6$, 435×10^6 and 335×10^6 maxwell.

It will be seen from Fig. 14 that two alternative versions of a machine of given size are possible both having the desired value of Φ_2 and power. In practice, however, only solutions to the left of the maximum are acceptable.

Formula 7 shows that maximum electromagnetic power is proportional to the square of the rotor flux. An increase in rotor flux density is therefore to be regarded as a rational means of increasing the power of a machine of given size. But only a small increase in maximum power can be achieved by increasing the flux density owing to saturation conditions. Any substantial increase in maximum power requires an increase in rotor diameter.

3. THE VARIATION OF THE CHARACTERISTICS OF ACTUAL TURBO-GENERATORS WITH INCREASING OUTPUT

Having considered these two imaginary series of turbo-generators which represent the limits within which actual turbo-generators can be built, a study will now be made of the maximum power of actual machines. It is essentially a question of relating the diameter of the rotor to the desired output.

In Fig. 15 the active power is plotted as the abscissa and the diameter of the rotor as the ordinate. The horizontal lines 1-3 and 4 define the calculated practical range of output for various rotor diameters. These diameters are currently used

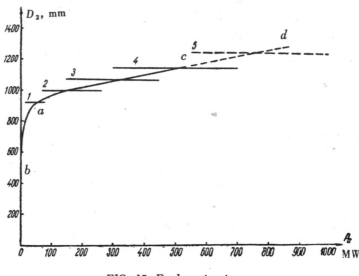

FIG. 15. Explanation in text

in Soviet designs. The maximum power in each range depends on the particular thermal conditions and the reactances x'_d and x''_d, since each range, considered alone, has roughly the same characteristics as a "series of constant frame size" (see Table 3). At low outputs a series of constant diameter is limited by the designer's desire to remain within the limits of rational machine utilization (i.e. to avoid excess capability) and by the deterioration in the characteristics of a generator when the ratio l_t/D_i falls below 2.5 to 3.0 [15]. At the lower end of each output range the degree of forced cooling is slight, but by the top of the range it has become considerable.

To determine the general relationship between rotor diameter and power, it is obviously necessary to consider typical intermediate machines and not those at the extremes of each range.

It will be seen from Fig. 15 that the mid points of all four

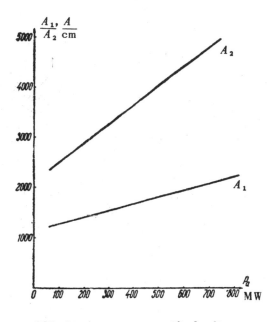

FIG. 16. A_1 — stator specific loading;
A_2 — rotor specific loading.

ranges lie along one straight line which as a first approximation
can be taken as the most rational relationship between diameter
and output. The curve $D_2 = f(P_a)$ may be continued to the region
of low outputs (the section *a-b*) from test data of actual machines.
The required increase in rotor diameter for higher outputs is
found by extrapolation. Thus, for 750 MW the appropriate diameter is 1250 mm. It has been calculated that the output range
for this diameter is that indicated by line 5. The need to increase the diameter to 1250 mm for outputs of the order of 750 MW
has been confirmed by a comparative analysis of 750 MW turbo-
generators with rotor diameters of 1075, 1150 and 1250 mm.
    The conclusion to be drawn from analysis of the relationship
$D_2 = f(Pa)$ and the cited design studies is that a larger rotor
diameter is definitely required for outputs of 500 to 750 MW.

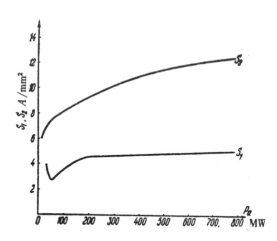

FIG. 17. S_1 — current density in stator winding;
S_2 — current density in rotor winding.

The probable characteristics of a "typical power progression series" of very large turbo-generators may now be deduced from the average relationship $D_2 = f(P_a)$.

The specific loadings A_1 and A_2 are illustrated in Fig. 16.

As regards the current density (Fig. 17), that of the stator windings s_1 remains practically constant above 200 MW, whereas that of the rotor s_2 gradually rises continually.

The uniformity of the stability characteristics of the machines in such a series is also interesting:

$$x''_d = 0.22 \overset{\mp}{}^{\,0.02} \text{ p.u.,}$$

$$x'_d = 0.34 \overset{\mp}{}^{\,0.04} \text{ p.u.,}$$

$$s_{\text{stat}} = 1.7 \overset{\mp}{}^{\,0.1} \text{ p.u.}$$

The large increase in excitation power also stands out (see Fig. 18).

It is therefore necessary to develop new sources of large d.c.

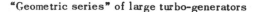

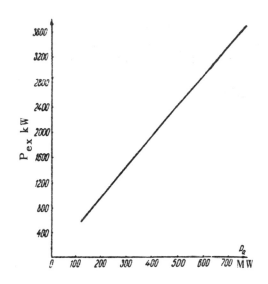

FIG. 18. Excitation power as a function of the active power of a
turbo-generator

supplies.

CONCLUSIONS

1. The foregoing theoretical analysis and study of actual turbo-generators with various outputs and rotor diameters has produced a mean curve which relates any rotor diameters to a particular range of outputs. Each corresponding series of machines can be regarded as a typical power progression series.

2. Extrapolation of this mean curve indicates that outputs of the order of 750 MW require a diameter of 1250 mm. This has been confirmed by a comparative analysis of designs with various diameters. It will be shown in section IV that such an increase can only be achieved by solving many other design and research problems.

3. A power progression series of machines is also a series

with uniform stability characteristics.

4. The increase in excitation power is approximately proportional to that of the active power of the generator.

CHAPTER IV

THE NEW PROBLEMS OF DESIGN

Turbo-generators are already being produced with high specific powers which feature larger gaps, rotor diameters of approximately maximum size, direct cooling of the winding copper and high pressure hydrogen in the casing. Design problems have now arisen which were previously not considered at all, or were thought to be solved on assumptions that were only applicable to relatively small machines. These new aspects of turbo-generator design will now be considered.

1. ELECTRICAL ANALYSIS

It has already been shown that an increase in the specific power of a turbo-generator involves increased specific current loadings which result in greater leakage fluxes. Therefore, it is necessary to refine the methods of analysing leakage fluxes in order to calculate the loss and reactance and determine the saturation of the machine.

(a) **Stray Losses.** The major stray loss, and one which is an important component of the total losses, is that occurring on the surface of the stator and rotor due to their harmonic m.m.f.'s of higher frequency. This calculation entails the determining of the magnetic induction of each stator harmonic m.m.f. on the surface of the rotor and vice versa.

The magnetic induction on the rotor surface due to the stator ν-th harmonic m.m.f. [18, 19] including the flux reduction factor and the eddy current reaction is

$$B_{\nu c} = \frac{\mu_0 A_1 \sqrt{(2)} \cdot k'_{w\nu}}{\dfrac{\nu \delta k_c}{R_c}} \cdot k_{\nu 1\text{-}2} \cdot k''_{r\nu}. \qquad (8)$$

The magnetic induction on the surface of the stator bore due to the rotor ν-the harmonic m.m.f. is

$$B_{\nu p} = \frac{2\mu_0 \cdot A_2 \cdot k''_{w\nu}}{\dfrac{\nu \delta k_c}{R_c}} k_{\nu\ 1\text{-}2} \cdot k'_{r\nu}. \tag{9}$$

In these formulae the coefficients $k_{\nu\ 1\text{-}2}$ and $k_{\nu 1\text{-}2}$ represent the attenuation of the ν-th harmonic across the gap, and $k'_{r\nu}$, $k''_{r\nu}$ the weakening of the field of the ν-th harmonic in the gap due to the eddy current reaction induced therein.

For large turbo-generators with gap lengths of the order of 5 to 10 per cent of the rotor radius, the coefficients $k_{\nu\ 1\text{-}2}$ and $k_{\nu\ 1\text{-}2}$ must take into account the slope of the field. This entails solving the equations of the electromagnetic field [21]

$$\text{rot } H_\nu = 0$$

and

$$\text{div } B_\nu = 0$$

in cylindrical co-ordinates and not in the customary Cartesian frame of reference.

The solution for these coefficients is

$$k\nu + 2_{-1} = \frac{\nu \delta k_c / R_c}{\left[\dfrac{(R_1/R_2)^{2\nu} - 1}{2\,(R_1/R_2)^{\nu} - 1}\right]}; \tag{10}$$

$$k_{\nu\ 1\ -\ 2} = \frac{\nu \delta k_c / R_c}{\left[\dfrac{(R_1/R_2)^{2\nu} - 1}{2\,(R_1/R_2)^{\nu + 1}}\right]}. \tag{10a}$$

With a Cartesian frame of reference, i.e. regarding the stator and rotor surfaces as planes, the solution is

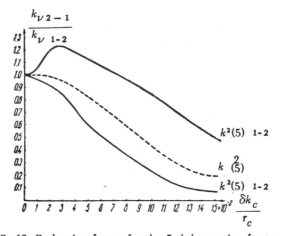

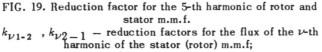

FIG. 19. Reduction factor for the 5-th harmonic of rotor and
stator m.m.f.

$k_{\nu 1\text{-}2}$, $k_{\nu 2-1}$ — reduction factors for the flux of the ν-th
harmonic of the stator (rotor) m.m.f;

$\delta k_c / \tau_c$ — ratio of gap to pole pitch.

$$k_\nu = \frac{\delta \nu k_c / R_c}{\sinh \delta \nu k_c / R_c}. \tag{11}$$

Figure 19 shows for the 5th harmonic the variation of the
quantities $k^2_{\nu\ 2\text{-}1}$, $k^2_{\nu\ 1\text{-}2}$ and k^2_ν as a function of $\delta k_c / \tau_c$,
which defines the rati o of the gap to the pole pitch.

It will be seen the curves in Fig. 19 that a mean value for
the coefficient k_ν would lead to considerable error. It is also
interesting to note that the coefficient $k_{\nu\ 1\text{-}2}$ can be greater
than 1 if $\delta k_c / \tau_c$ is small. The explanation is the higher con-
centration on the rotor surface of the ν-th harmonic stator flux
due to the smaller area compared with that of the stator bore.

The weakening of the field must also be considered if the
magnitude and structure of the stray loss in the iron is to be

accurately determined and if a correct comparison is to be made between the various design alternatives. If the reduction of stator and rotor tooth harmonics is ignored, the losses in machines with a small number of slots are considerably over-stated.

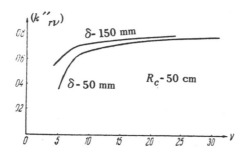

FIG. 20. The square of the reaction coefficient as a function of the order of the harmonic

It is usual practice to assume that the reaction coefficients $k'_{r\nu}$ and $k''_{r\nu}$ are constant for all harmonics, and then the coefficient $k'_{r\nu}$, which relates to laminated iron, is further assumed to be approximately 1. As regards $k''_{r\nu}$, the eddy current reaction factor in the rotor iron, its value depends on the quantities δ and R_c [20] in addition to the properties of the iron and the order of the harmonic. However, calculations show that there is practically no variation in the coefficients $k''_{r\nu}$ for generators with large gaps for any harmonic except the fifth and seventh.

Figure 20 illustrates the relationship $[k''_{r\nu}]^2 = f(\nu)$ for a generator with a rotor diameter of 1000 mm and gaps of 50 and 150 mm (the extreme gap lengths of large turbo-generators).

The curves in Fig. 20 indicate that $k''_{r\nu}$ is almost independent of ν or δ.

In large turbo-generators another important component of stray loss is the additional loss in the stator winding copper due to the eddy currents induced by the slot leakage flux (i.e. the loss due to the non-uniform current distribution in the conductors). The proportion of these losses increases considerably if the winding conductors consist fully or partially of tubular subconductors (Fig. 12, b) containing the cooling liquid or gas. The height of tubular subconductors must be much greater than that of the normal strips from hydraulic considerations and since

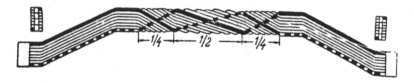

FIG. 21. 540° transposition

the additional loss is proportional to the cube of the subconductors' height, the increase in loss is considerable. Designs have therefore been developed (Fig. 12 c, d) in which the liquid (gas) flows only through some of the subconductors, the remainder being of thinner copper strip.

In calculating the additional losses in a bar consisting of several types of subconductor, the conventional notion of a field coefficient is unacceptable since the loss from the displacement of current in a particular subconductor depends on the currents in all the other subconductors. Thus the loss from displacement of current in any subconductor is no longer proportional to its internal impedance loss and the formulae for calculating the eddy current loss must be correspondingly modified. It should, however, be noted that there is very little difference between the additional loss (in Watts) in a tubular conductor and that in a solid conductor of the same external dimensions (usually less than 10 per cent).

Calculations which have been made for large generators show that at outputs greater than 400 to 500 MW the marked increase in additional losses in bars with tubular subconductors makes it advisable to use bars having special cooling tubes (Fig. 12, a, d), although the manufacturing difficulties are so complex that such systems are only adopted with reluctance at the present time. Experience has shown that insufficient care in insulating the internal tubes from the copper conductors leads to short circuits which cause a considerably greater stray loss even though they are not actually dangerous.

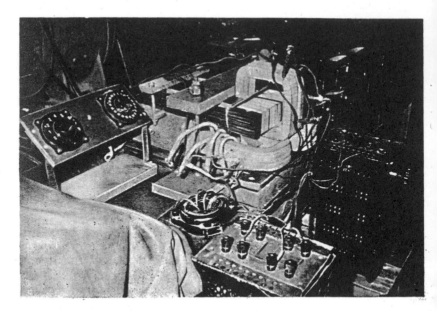

FIG. 22. Model for investigating the stray losses in the teeth
of end core packet

Increased output with a constant diameter also results in
rapid increase in various kinds of stray loss in the stator end
regions. In fact, if the increase in amplitude of the harmonic gap
fluxes is limited at higher outputs by compensating increase in
the gap length (formulae (8), (9)), the magnetic permeance of
the stator end regions remains practically unchanged and the
leakage fluxes increase in direct proportion to output. Reference should also be made to the eddy current loss in the stator
end regions due to an absence of transposition in the winding
overhang. The eddy currents which are induced in the overhang
by the fundamental leakage field flow through the whole winding
and cause additional loss which increases greatly with increasing output. Use has been made abroad of "540° transposition" to
reduce this loss component (see Fig. 21).

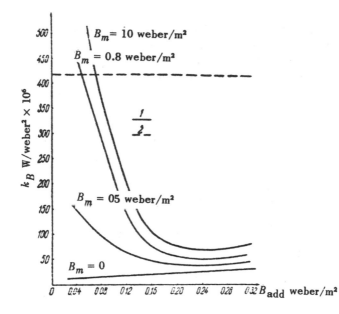

FIG. 23. Losses in tooth of end packet (from test results on model):

$$k_B = Q_{qz}/B^2_{add} \cdot b^3_z \cdot h_z \; ;$$

B_{add} — additional flux on tooth surface,
b_z — tooth width,
h_z — tooth height;
B_m — density of main flux in tooth.
1 — values of k_B found from tests on tooth model:
2 — values of k_B for the same model calculated
    from Winchester's loss formula [23] (at 50 c/s)

However, such a solution is only to be regarded as acceptable for high outputs owing to the constructional complications. The stator winding overhang is also affected by the rotating end region leakage field of the rotor. In this connexion the overhang is sometimes regarded [22] as a solid block of copper and the loss therein is determined as in a copper sheet with the skin effect included.

In the early days of turbo-generator design, the stray losses in the extreme end packets of the stator, in the clamping plates and the fingers formed a considerable proportion of the total loss [18]. Now that there has been a changeover to non-magnetic end bells and clamping plates, this type of loss no longer has much effect on the efficiency of the generator, although it may be a source of local hot spots (mainly in the teeth of the stator end packet) under conditions of under-excitation, or even under rated conditions in large generators.

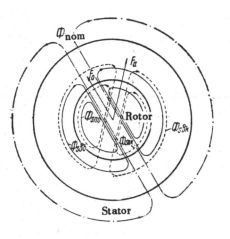

FIG. 24. Direction of the rotor
fluxes for rated conditions

The stray loss in the end packets and clamping plates is difficult to measure owing to the complexity· of the magnetic fields in the end regions and the difficulties in determining the eddy currents and loss due to particular magnetic fields. These fields may be found graphically, analytically [22] or by modelling in an electrolytic tank [28].

It is best to investigate losses in relation to leakage flux by physical models since very great difficulties arise in tests on an actual generator in operation.

Figure 22 shows a photograph of a model which has been developed at the Electromechanics Institute for determining the variation in the loss in the teeth of an end packet with the flux density of the leakage field and the main field.

In particular, tests have revealed that the eddy current circuit is non-linear and that the flux density of the main field in an end packet has a great effect on the extent of additional losses (see Fig. 23).

In this connexion it should be noted that Winchester [23] failed to consider all the foregoing factors and his formula for the additional loss in the teeth cannot therefore be considered reliable.

In general, however, the available test data in this field are so meagre that the reliability of calculations is often reduced because the design engineer is compelled to use correction coefficients which have been obtained on other types of machine with other materials etc. It is therefore very important to continue to accumulate actual and model test data.

(b) **The interaction between the main flux and leakage fluxes.** One consequence of an increased leakage flux is that rated conditions can no longer be found in the usual way from the no load and short circuit characteristics without running the risk of error. This is of major importance in the problem of determining the full load rotor current. It is normal to calculate the magnetic flux in the rotor teeth and body from the sum of the gap flux and the rotor internal leakage flux when operating on no load. By considering the pattern of the fluxes in the rotor under rated conditions, it is possible to include the effect of the rotor leakage flux corresponding to the armature reaction current and also the deviation of the flux axis from the rotor polar axis under operating conditions (Fig. 24).

Such calculations provide correction coefficients for the rotor current (k_i) and excitation loss (k_q) under rated conditions which are superior to the results obtained from a Potier diagram. They vary in value with the saturation of the rotor body (in Table 4 this is the flux density $B_{z(0.2)}$ on no load at a voltage equal to the internal e.m.f. at a point 0.2 of the tooth length from the bottom of the slot).

In generators with large gaps it is necessary to consider the fundamental gap leakage flux. For a two-pole machine the ratio of the flux from the rotor to that entering the stator (neglecting curvature of the surface) is

TABLE 4

$B_z(0.2)$	up to 20,000 G	23,000 G	27,000 G
k_i ...	1.0	1.03 to 1.05	1.06 to 1.07
k_q ...	1.0	1.06 to 1.1	1.12 to 1.15

$$\frac{\Phi_{rot}}{\Phi_{stat}} \approx \cosh \frac{\delta}{R_c} \tag{12}$$

or

$$\frac{\Phi_{rot}}{\Phi_{stat}} \approx 1 + \frac{\delta}{R_c} \tag{12a}$$

Neglect of the term δ/R_c in generators with gap lengths of the order of 100 mm may under-estimate the actual flux density of the rotor teeth and these are the most heavily saturated parts of the magnetic circuit.

It is more logical to calculate the rated stator iron loss at a voltage equal to the internal e.m.f. E'_v rather than at rated voltage, which results in an increase by a factor of $(E'_v)^2$. This factor could formerly be ignored, but for the generators which are considered in part 3 of this section it may amount to 20 to 30 per cent.

2. MECHANICAL STRENGTH AND RUNNING STABILITY

It has already been pointed out that turbo-generators are subjected to heavy mechanical, thermal and electromagnetic stress. A study of the mechanical strength and critical vibration is essential since many new theoretical problems arise at very high outputs and with increased rotor utilization. Some of these problems will now be considered.

(a) **Determination of maximum rotor diameter from considerations of mechanical strength and including ductility.** It has
been shown that an increase in rotor diameter can considerably
improve the characteristics of a generator. But it still has to be
proved that a change from a diameter of 1075-1150 mm to one of
1200-1250 mm is a practicable proposition. In other words, it has
to be proved that the present factors of safety can be reduced.
A study of American practice shows that the factors of safety
provided in the U.S.S.R. can be reduced.

An increase in rotational speed is one way of increasing the
output of electrical machines per unit of volume, i.e.

$$P = cD^2 ln. \tag{13}$$

But in turbo-generator design it is necessary to consider the
factor of safety and this leads to a somewhat different conclusion.
It is known from the theory of elasticity that the stress at any
point of a rotated rotor is given by the expression :

$$\sigma \equiv D^2 n^2. \tag{14}$$

Assuming that the shape of the rotor remains unchanged, that
the specific weight of its individual parts is constant, and that
$\sigma \equiv$ const (i.e. that the factor of safety is constant), a change
in rotational speed requires a corresponding change in diameter
in the ratio

$$\frac{L}{D_I} = \frac{n_I}{n}. \tag{15}$$

Accordingly, if the length l and utilization coefficient c are
the same, the power on changing to the speed n_1 is:

$$P = cD_I^2 ln_I = cD^2 \left(\frac{n}{n_I}\right)^2 ln_I = cD^2 ln \left(\frac{n}{n_I}\right) = P \frac{n}{n_I}. \tag{16}$$

This result can be formulated in the following way. On increasing the rotational speed of a turbo-generator with a constant mechanical stress, the body diameter must be reduced in proportion to the increase in speed; the output per unit length must also be reduced in the same ratio if the specific electric and magnetic loading A and B remain unchanged. Thus, an increase in rotational speed does not itself increase the unit output of a generator. Nevertheless, it is known that American companies have already produced very high-power generators. How has this been done ?

A study of a recent foreign publication [24] has shown that unit output has been increased in the U.S.A. by allowing an increased level of mechanical stresses in the rotor body and end bell assembly, i.e. by accepting a lower factor of safety than in the U.S.S.R.

It must be emphasized that lower factors of safety demand forgings of better quality and improved fault detection. The serious breakdowns which have occurred in a number of American power stations may be repeated unless these conditions are fulfilled. In the opinion of authoritative foreign specialists [25], these breakdowns could have been avoided by appropriate casting and inspection techniques. In the design of large turbo-generators, special attention must therefore be paid to the perfection of the methods of inspecting forgings as well as to the improvement of casting methods (e.g. vacuum casting).

Westinghouse has made a thorough investigation on models and in actual conditions to determine the permissible stresses in rotor units. The following propositions are now accepted in turbo-generator design in the U.S.A.

1. The criterion of the strength of a rotor is the mean tangential stress in the body and not the maximum tangential stress at the bore.

2. From tests on models and experience with the overspeeding of turbo-generators, the maximum permissible tangential bore stress of a rotor is: 50 to 60 per cent and 72 to 86 per cent of the yield point for normal speed and 20 per cent overspeed respectively. This latter figure corresponds to a factor of safety

of 1.15 which is 30 per cent below the figure of 1.7 specified in the U.S.S.R. Further study is required to verify these arguments, but it is now at least possible to point to the beginnings of a theory which indirectly confirms the possibility of allowing an increased degree of mechanical stress. The theory of elastic-plastic deformation [26, 27] which has been developed extensively by foreign and Soviet writers, now provides a picture of the stresses in rotating disks which are partially or fully transformed into the plastic state.

Mathematical and theoretical studies at the Electromechanics Institute have shown that there is a considerable difference in loading between the initiation of yield at the bore of the disk and the start of yielding at the external rim. The residual deformation at the bore is quite small when yield occurs at the external radius (about 0.5 per cent) and there is a long way to go before final failure occurs.

As regards the properties of the metal, that used in the U.S.A. for the rotor and end bell forgings has approximately the same yield point and ultimate tensile strength as that in the U.S.S.R. ($\sigma_s/\sigma_B = 62/73$ kg/mm²).

A thorough study of the possibilities of increasing rotor diameters for maximum turbo-generator output therefore deserves consideration.

The strength of the rotor end bell presents a special problem in so far as the maximum tangential stresses at the bore are close to their mean value owing to the small difference between the end bell radii R_{1eb}/R_{2eb} ($R_{1eb}/R_{2eb} \cong 1$). Hence a change to a large diameter is not always possible. It has been calculated that the self-stress due to the end bell itself is the main component of the total tangential stress. The centrifugal force is given by the expression

$$\sigma \equiv \gamma R^2_{eb} n^2, \tag{17}$$

where γ is the specific weight of the end bell material.

Provided the 'shape is geometrically similar, the factor of

strength for end bells made from the various materials is given by the expression

$$k = \frac{\sigma_s}{c R^2_{eb}\, n^2 \gamma}. \qquad (18)$$

The factor of strength is unaltered on changing to a different material if

$$\frac{\sigma_{s1}}{R^2_{1eb}\gamma_1} = \frac{\sigma_{s2}}{R^2_{2eb}\gamma_2}, \qquad (19)$$

and therefore

$$\frac{\sigma_{s2}}{\gamma_2} = \frac{\sigma_{s1}}{\gamma_1}\left(\frac{R_{2eb}}{R_{1eb}}\right)^2. \qquad (20)$$

Thus, on changing to a different diameter with the same geometric proportions of the end bell (i.e. ratio R_{1eb}/R_{2eb}), the factor of strength of the material, defined as the ratio of its yield point to its specific weight, must be varied in proportion to the square of the ratio of the rotor body diameter. Bearing in mind what has been said about reducing the factor of safety of the rotor body in the ratio of 1.7 to 1.15, the rotor diameter should be increased (for the same geometric proportions) in the ratio

$$\frac{R_{2eb}}{R_{1eb}} = \sqrt{\left(\frac{1.7}{1.15}\right)} = 1.22,$$

i.e. the practical rotor diameter is

$$D_2 = 1075 \times 1.22 = 1310 \text{ mm}.$$

The corresponding factor of strength for the end bell is

$$\frac{\sigma_{S2}}{\gamma_2} = \frac{\sigma_{S1}}{\gamma_1} \left(\frac{R'_2}{R'_1} \right)^2 = \frac{9000}{7.8} \left(\frac{1310}{1075} \right)^2 = 1700 \, .$$

It will be seen by comparing the factors of strength of the various materials listed in Table 5 that titanium alloys are the most promising. These ensure high factors of strength and thereby provide further scope for increasing the diameter of the rotor.

TABLE 5

Material	Yield point kg/cm²	Specific weight g/cm³	Factor of strength
Nickel steel for end bells	9000	7.8	1150
Duralumin . . .	3000	2.7	1110
Titanium alloys	9000	4.5	2000

One of the most important problems in the production of rotor end bells is that of selecting the right method of seating the support ring on the rotor. Three main principles can be used:

1 — a seating solely on the outboard centering ring with the end of the bell clear of the rotor body (see Fig.25 a);
2 — seating solely on the rotor body ("cantilever seating") (Fig. 25, b);
3 — combined seating of the end bell on the rotor body and on the centering ring through intermediate resilient elements (Fig. 25, c); this also includes seating on an intermediate bush (Metropolitan-Vickers, Fig. 25, d).

The advantages and disadvantages of these methods are compared in Table 6.

The particular advantages of one or another method can only be decided from test results after extensive research.

A special study must be made of the seating problem with titanium alloy end bells in view of their higher ductility and special methods must be evolved.

The prospect of rotors with a fully embedded excitation

TABLE 6

Method	Advantages	Disadvantages	By whom and where used
1.	The most favourable mechanical operating conditions for the end bell. No electrical contact between end bell and rotor.	Relative movement between end bell and winding resulting in increased insulation wear.	Elektrosila U.S.S.R, and General Electric on small machines.
2.	Favourable operating conditions for the end bell mechanically. More reliable support of the winding overhang.	Electrical contact between support ring and rim of rotor body which may cause arcing or pitting of end bell seating due to damping currents. Complicated axial locking of the end bell (annular keys).	Kharkov Electrical Engineering Works, Brown Boveri, B.T.H.
3.	Simple production and erection of end bell assembly.	The end bell is subjected to considerable radial forces and skewing which may lead to the destruction of the seatings or intermediate resilient elements.	Elektrosila and General Electric.

winding in both the slots and the overhang are very alluring. It would no longer be necessary to search for special alloys and the question of end bell seating, one of the most difficult design and production problems, would not arise. But in their place other difficulties are introduced which require special research.

The Electromechanics Institute has already studied a number

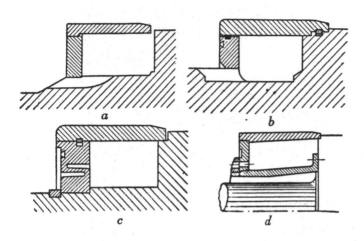

FIG. 25. Methods of fixing end bell assembly ($a - d$)

of such designs and one has already been patented [28].

(b) **Rotor critical speed.** Approximate methods of determining the critical speeds of turbo-generators were developed a long time ago, but work is continuing on the refinement of these methods since the operating speed of modern turbo-generators is quite close to the second critical speed. Factors which were formerly neglected are now included, e.g. the varying rigidity of the rotor on its two axes, the deformation of the bearings, and the effect of the rotor winding. To calculate the critical speed exactly, it is also necessary to consider the "coupling" between the generator and turbine which in large sets has three or four cylinders. Fig. 26 a, shows the shaft deflection of a 200 MW set neglecting the bearing deformation [29].

Methods have now been perfected for calculating critical speeds exactly using electronic computers [30], flexible scale models, and analogues in the form of capacitance-inductance circuits [31].

(c) **The resonant frequency of the stator casing.** An increase in rotor diameter favourably affects the critical speed of the rotor

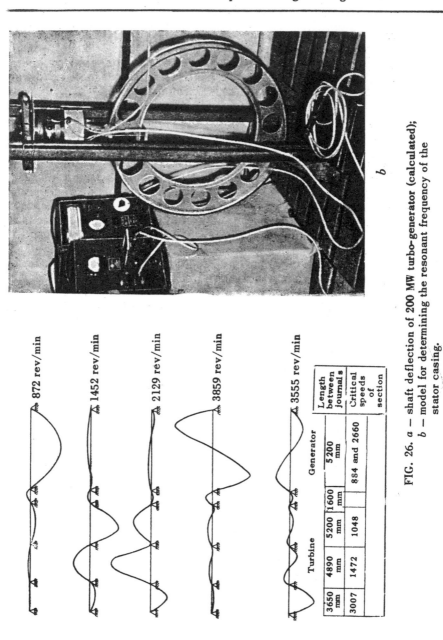

| 872 rev/min |
| 1452 rev/min |
| 2129 rev/min |
| 3859 rev/min |
| 3555 rev/min |

	Turbine		Generator	
Length between journals	3650 mm	4890 mm	5200 mm	1600 mm	5200 mm
Critical speeds of section	3007	1472	1048		884 and 2660

FIG. 26. *a* — shaft deflection of 200 MW turbo-generator (calculated); *b* — model for determining the resonant frequency of the stator casing.

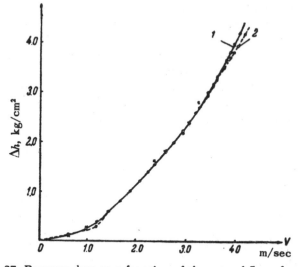

FIG. 27. Pressure drop as a function of the rate of flow of water
in a duct.
1 — test curve;   2 — calculated curve

shaft since the dangerous second critical speed is increased.
Conversely, an increase in the geometric dimensions of the
stator casing brings the resonant frequency of the casing closer
to that of the main disturbing force (100 c/s).

This matter has been specially studied on scale models at
the Electromechanics Institute [38]. Modelling theory has led to
the standard formula

$$k_f = \frac{1}{k_R} \sqrt{\frac{k_E}{k_\gamma}}, \qquad (21)$$

where k is a scale factor for frequency f, E is the modulus of
elasticity, R a geometric dimension (radius ?) and γ the specific
weight.

It is desirable to fulfill the condition $k_f = 1$. For this, use may be made of clear plastic models to the scale of 1/5 : 1/7.

It will be seen from the standard formula that if the geometric dimensions are increased in proportion, the resonant frequency of the casing decreases in inverse proportion to the geometric dimensions and therefore tends towards the frequency of the disturbing force. In this connexion it has become necessary to study the possibility of producing "flexible" casings with a lower resonant frequency than the disturbing force.

A plexiglass model which has been made at the Electromechanics Institute is shown in Fig. 26, b. The model represents a section of a 200 MW turbo-generator casing to a sixth scale.

3. THERMAL AND HYDRAULIC ANALYSIS OF DIRECT COOLING

The temperature rise of the windings and the pressure drop of the cooling medium in the ducts of the conductors are calculated from the results of electrical analysis and a study of the design. The heat loss in the windings and the dimensions of the internal ducts are thereby determined.

The analytical problem is that of determining the appropriate pressure head for the required rate of flow of the cooling medium in the ducts and the temperature rise of the copper at this desired rate of flow. Practical methods employ empirical relationships of hydraulics and heat transfer [30-34].

The simplest way of determining the pressure drop is to use the Darcy formula (see glossary for notation):

$$\Delta h = \xi_f \frac{l}{d} \frac{\rho v^2}{2}. \tag{22}$$

From test results of a water-cooled stator slot model at the Elektromechanics Institute, formula 22 is sufficiently accurate for practical purposes (Fig. 27). The only exception is in the zone of indeterminate flow of the fluid in the duct where the corresponding rate of flow was 1 to 1.4 m/sec.

Formula 22 only holds for long ducts such as those in the stator windings of turbo-generators. For short ducts, where local pressure losses are more important, the pressure drop in the individual ducts may be found by the following formula:

$$\Delta h = \left(\xi_f \frac{l}{d} + n\xi_r + \xi_{in} + \xi_{out} \right) \frac{\rho v^2}{2g}. \tag{23}$$

(see glossary for notation).

The temperature rise of the winding copper is based on the assumption that all the heat of the winding is transferred to the cooling medium flowing in the internal ducts. The actual temperature rise is taken as the sum of the individual temperature drops along the thermal flow path. If the cooling medium is in direct contact with the copper of each conductor, the copper temperature rise depends only on two components, namely, the temperature rise of the cooling medium and the temperature drop at the duct. The maximum copper temperature rise is usually considered on the basis of the heat loss in one duct at a given rate of flow. The maximum temperature rise of the cooling medium in the duct is then determined by the formula

$$\Delta t_1 = \frac{P}{cQ}, \tag{24}$$

which is derived from the heat balance equation.

The temperature drop at the surface of the copper is found by a similar formula

$$\Delta t_2 = \frac{P}{aF}. \tag{24a}$$

The heat dissipating surface F can be found without difficulty for any type of duct. The heat transfer coefficient a can be found by determining the Nusselt number

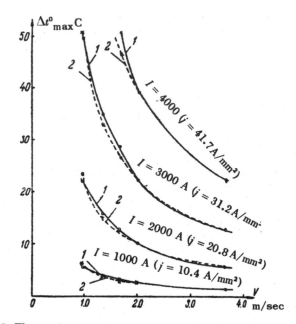

FIG. 28. The maximum copper temperature rise for various current
densities as a function of the rate of water flow.
1 — test curve;   2 — calculated curve

$$a = \frac{Nu\lambda}{d}.$$

The Nusselt number is in fact calculated by the following
empirical formula for turbulent flow:

$$Nu = 0.023 \cdot Re^{0.8} \cdot Pr^{0.4}$$

or for laminar flow

$$Nu = 0.74 \, (Re \cdot Pr)^{0.2} (Pr \cdot Gr)^{0.1}$$

The maximum temperature rise of the copper is

$$\Delta t_m = \Delta t_1 + \Delta t_2 . \tag{25}$$

If part of the conductor is not in direct contact with the cooling medium (Fig. 12, *a*, *c*, *d*), the maximum temperature rise of the copper will occur at the furthest point from the ventilation ducts. The maximum temperature rise will then have a third component, namely, the temperature drop from the stated point to the duct surface. The internal temperature drop in the conductor copper itself can as a rule be ignored. The total temperature drop for the third component is then the sum of the drops in the individual layers of insulation along the heat flow path from the conductor furthest from the duct surface:

$$\Delta t_3 = \sum \frac{p_k \delta_k}{\lambda_k F_k} . \tag{26}$$

The maximum temperature rise of winding copper is then:

$$\Delta t_m = \Delta t_1 + \Delta t_2 + \Delta t_3 . \tag{27}$$

From tests on the cited model of a stator winding slot (Fig. 28), this is quite an accurate method of determining the temperature rise of the copper.

The discrepancy between calculated and test values of the pressure drop and copper temperature rise is due to incorrect formulae since the actual conditions for the motion of the cooling medium and heat transfer in the ducts have varied as the medium is not at the same temperature at all points in the ducts and, as a corrollary, the physical characteristics of the medium vary along the flow path.

As regards the conditions of heat transfer, the temperature of the copper is not the same over the entire length of the conductors owing to the heating of the cooling medium as it flows along the ducts. Consequently, the intensity of heat generation varies and there is an axial transfer of heat in the conductor.

Further research on small and full scale models and proto-type machines is required before the formulae can be improved to include these features.

4. EXCITATION SYSTEMS

Until recently in the U.S.S.R., the excitation winding of the generator has been supplied exclusively from a d.c. generator connected direct to the shaft of the main set. This system has been completely reliable and convenient. But the maximum output of d.c. generators at 3000 rev/min is between 300 and 500 kW, depending on commutation conditions and mechanical strength. Such outputs are only suitable for 150-200 MW turbo-generators. The industry is therefore confronted with the problem of devising new d.c. supply sources for turbo-generator excitation.

In America and Great Britain, exciters connected to the turbo-generator shaft via a reduction gear have been used to a certain extent. The projected tandem-shaft 550 MW set in Great Britain has two machine exciters driven through reduction gears. This arrangement is of a certain interest in that it allows the maximum power of an exciter to be increased. Separately driven exciters have also been used to about the same extent. The drive is usually an induction motor which is supplied from the power station bus or from a synchronous generator connected to the shaft of the main generator. Separate machine-exciter sets have the following merits:

1. Large low-speed exciters with great mechanical and commutation reliability can be produced.

2. Repairs and inspection can be carried out without stopping the turbo-generator.

3. The exciter set can be accommodated in any convenient place inside or outside the engine room.

Their main disadvantages are the undue complication of the overall system of excitation and the reduction in reliability owing to the special drive motor which is supplied from the station auxiliaries. In order to ensure stable performance during fault conditions, the exciter set must have a motor with a high maximum pull-out torque and an enormous flywheel.

A comparison of the characteristics of d.c. generators supplying rolling mill motors with those required for an exciter set (Fig. 18) shows that their use for very large turbo-generators over 300 MW must be regarded as highly improbable owing to their great weight and size.

The excitation of turbo-generators from a.c. sources via a rectifier is now being developed in two directions:

1. From a high frequency (inductor-type) generator on the shaft of the main set through semiconductor rectifiers;

2. From the terminals of the turbo-generator via a stepdown transformer and controlled mercury arc rectifiers.

A detailed comparison of these systems has already been published in the U.S.S.R. [17]. It need only be mentioned here that the development of these systems is only being held up by the inadequate operating reliability of semiconductor rectifiers and sealed mercury arc rectifiers. It has recently been proposed to develop a brushless system of excitation and energize the rotor via a "dynamic transformer". This requires the accomodation of the rectifying device on the rotor of the turbo-generator. There are difficulties in using existing rectifiers for this system at large outputs, but it may be a different matter if very small high temperature semiconductor elements can be produced. The advantage of the arrangement is that the turns of the rotor winding can be connected in parallel. If this is done, the voltage is reduced, the number of turns in the slot is decreased, the slot space factor is improved, but the magnitude of the current increases so much for large generators that excitation systems using brushes cannot be used.

5. PROSPECTS OF NEW MATERIALS

Technical progress in electrical engineering is closely related to the improvement of existing materials and the introduction of new materials. Progress is now being made in the following directions:

(a) improved stator winding insulation;
(b) The use of cold-rolled grain-oriented steel with improved properties;
(c) the utilization of special copper alloys to improve the strength of the rotor winding; and
(d) the use of materials with a low specific weight for the end bell assembly.

The task of improving the insulation is primarily necessitated by the demand for higher voltages with increasing unit outputs. An increase in output at constant voltage results in correspondingly larger currents, heavier switchgear and large current conductors on the L.T. side of the station. Micanite is not sufficiently reliable for the slot insulation at voltages greater than 22-24 kV. Work is therefore continuing on the development of new types of insulation, mainly by substituting thermo-setting resins for the bituminous varnishes used in micanite. The use of thermo-setting resins eliminate the air bubbles which form inside the insulation when the solvent in bituminous varnish evaporates.

In recent years, announcements have appeared abroad concerning new types of insulation using thermo-setting resins ("thermalastic", "micapal", "orlitsa"). Their insulating properties are apparently superior to those of micanite (Fig. 29), but there is still no news of any foreign generators over 22 to 24 kV.

Incidentally, if the new types of insulation will also allow an improved slot space factor, this can considerably reduce the winding loss. However, an increase in permissible operating temperature of insulation is not so important for large turbo-generators as for other types of electrical machine owing to the use of direct cooling.

The idea of a high-voltage oil-filled turbo-generator with cable insulation has already been referred to. The practicability of such a machine can only be judged by experience.

The use of cold-rolled grain-oriented steel in particular, and improvements in the properties of the stator laminations in general, can bring about an appreciable reduction in weight and size as well as reduce losses. The magnetic permeance of cold-rolled grain-oriented steel is high and specific losses are reduced when the flux is in the direction of rolling. Moreover, owing to its uniform gauge, the utilization factor can be increased and the assembly of the core is better.

These characteristics have led to the extensive use of cold-rolled grain-oriented steel in transformers since the magnetic circuit of a transformer can be arranged so that the flux is almost entirely in the direction of rolling. The use of cold-rolled grain-oriented steel in rotating machines has been delayed because the flux is always in two mutually perpendicular directions (tooth and core) in the same segment so that full advantage cannot be taken of the material. Research is now in progress to reduce the uni-directional nature of cold-rolled grain-oriented steel and to impart the same properties in all directions. However, there are good prospects for the use of cold-rolled grain-oriented steel in rotating machines even with its marked uni-directional property

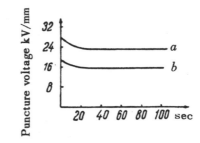

FIG. 29. Comparative data of life tests at 180°C:
a — insulation with thermo-setting resin (thermalastic);
b — insulation with bituminous varnish.

If the stator stampings of a turbo-generator are made from cold-rolled grain-oriented steel, the segments may be so arranged that the direction of rolling coincides with that of the magnetic flux in the yoke where the weight of steel and losses are much greater than in the teeth. But, at very large outputs when the losses in the active belt increase sharply owing to the higher specific loading, it may be advisable to adopt other methods, e.g. arranging the teeth in the direction of rolling or a "mixed assembly" in which the cross and lengthwise stamped sheets are arranged alternately in a particular order.

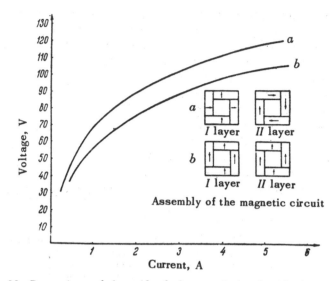

FIG. 30. Comparison of the no load characteristics (*a*, *b*) of two transformers with magnetic circuits made from grade E330 cold-rolled grain-
oriented electrical steel

This method reduces the total magnetic reluctance of the
core stampings, i.e. it increases the flux density for the same
m.m.f. across the stator stampings. The relationship between the
m.m.f. and flux density can be illustrated by no load tests on two transformers in which the magnetic circuits were arranged in such a
way (Fig. 30) that one (version *a*) resembled the core of a rotating machine with "mixed assembly", whilst the other (version *b*) was arranged in the conventional manner for rotating
machines. It will be seen from Fig. 30 that for the same flux
density the m.m.f. is much less in version *a* whilst the iron loss
is practically identical.

To assess the effect of using various assembly arrangements,
a comparative analysis has been made of four methods of assembly on a 500 MW generator (Table 7):

1) hot-rolled E4AA grade electrical steel;

TABLE 7

Data	Method of assembly			
	1	2	3	4
Turbo generator output, MW	500	500	500	500
Grade of stator steel, stamping and assembly method	E4AA	E330 teeth transverse to rolling	E330 teeth in direction of rolling	E330 mixed assembly
Overall loss $Q_{Cul} + Q_{Cud*} + Q_{Fe**}$,kW	1730	1690	1575	1565
Weight of steel in stator yoke, metric tons[t]	152	120	138	120
Weight of steel in stator teeth, metric tons	28.1	28.1	24.0	24.0
Weight of copper in stator winding, metric tons	22.2	22.2	27.7	27.7

* Additional stray loss in copper.
** Main losses at a voltage equal to the internal m.m.f.,
[t] 1 metric ton = 2204 lb.

2) cold-rolled grain-oriented grade E330 steel with teeth across the direction of rolling;
3) the same, but with teeth along the direction of rolling;
4) the same, but with 1/3 of the sheets with teeth along, and 2/3 of the sheets with teeth across, the direction of rolling.

This Table indicates that versions 3 and 4 are little better than No. 2, but it should be pointed out that there is still a lack of test data regarding the use of cold-rolled grain-oriented steel, turbo-generator stray losses etc.

Of the new materials for use in turbo-generators, reference should be made to copper with a small silver content which increases the mechanical strength of the rotor winding, a part which is subjected to considerable mechanical stresses both by centrifugal forces and thermo-mechanical stresses.

The alloy "cond-al" (aluminium with small additions of iron, magnesium and silicon) is occasionally used abroad for rotor windings. But although this has improved mechanical properties compared with aluminium with the same specific weight and electrical conductivity, it is hardly likely to be used for turbo-generators in the range of outputs which are under consideration, since this would cause a considerable increase in the rotor winding loss.

Finally, reference should again be made to the prospects for the use of titanium for the rotor end bell. Its advantage over steel is its lower specific weight (see above). There is news of promising research being carried out into the use of titanium alloys by foreign firms engaged in the production of turbo-generators.

CHAPTER V

DESIGN STUDY OF A SINGLE-SHAFT 750 MW TURBO-GENERATOR

To assess the prospects for further increases in unit output and to see more exactly what this involves, the Electromechanics Institute jointly with works' design engineers has studied a single-shaft turbo-generator of 750 MW output which could later be raised to 1000 MW. The technical specification is as follows.

RATING

Rated active power	750,000 kW
Power factor	0.9
Rated voltage	27,000 V
Rated current	17,825 A
Winding phase connexion	star
Short circuit ratio	0.68
Steady state overload capability	1.83
Efficiency	98.97 %
Number of parallel circuits in stator winding	2

STATOR DIMENSIONS

Outside diameter of core	3170 mm
Length of core	6350 mm
Inside diameter of core	1550 mm
Type of core plate	E330 (cold-rolled), gauge 0.5 mm
Number of slots	54
Dimensions of slot	270 × 50 mm
Number of bars per slot	2

Total thickness of slot insulation (one side)   9 mm
Thickness of stator packet   60 mm
Dimensions of ventilation ducts   90 × 10
Dimensions of conductor strips   2.44 × 5.5

ROTOR DIMENSIONS

Diameter of body   1250 mm
Length of body   6500 mm
Number of slots   44/56
Gap   150 mm
Slot dimensions   182 × 31.7 mm
Number of turns in slot   9
Number of coils per pole   11
Dimensions of conductors   28 × 14,
                                                       internal
                                                       channel 12 × 6

ELECTROMAGNETIC LOADS

Specific loading of stator   1975 A/cm
Specific loading of rotor   4925 A/cm
Gap flux density   9600 G
Current density in stator winding   5.06 A/mm^2
Current density in rotor winding   12.00 A/mm^2

EXCITATION

Excitation current on load   3830 A
Excitation voltage   1000 V

LOSSES

Stator winding loss   1070 kW
Stator iron loss   663 kW
No load stray loss   468.0 kW
Short circuit stray loss   1183 kW

Excitation loss	3435 kW
Mechanical loss	1002.5 kW
Total losses	7822.0 kW

ROTOR COOLING SYSTEM

Quantity of winding cooling water	28.5 litre/sec
Water velocity in winding ducts	2 m/sec
Temperature rise of water in winding	27.7°C
Maximum temperature rise of copper	30°C
Pressure drop in winding	1/14 kg/cm^2
Maximum temperature of copper	70°C

THE STATOR WINDING COOLING SYSTEM

Quantity of winding cooling water	22.4 litre/sec
Water velocity in the winding ducts	2.0 m/sec
Pressure drop in winding (4 bars in series)	2.91 kg/cm^2
Temperature rise of water in winding	16.6°C
Maximum temperature rise of copper	35.8°C
Maximum temperature of copper	76.5°C

THE STATOR CORE COOLING SYSTEM

Hydrogen pressure in casing	3 atm
Volume of gas circulated	28 m^3/sec
Necessary pressure head	127 mm Hg (hydrogen 4 atm)
Maximum temperature of stator core packet	106.5°C
Temperature of cooled hydrogen	37.14°C
Temperature rise of gas in the machine	17.7°C

REACTANCE AND TIME CONSTANTS

Direct axis synchronous reactance	186.7%
Direct axis transient reactance	35%
Direct axis sub-transient reactance	22.3%

Open circuit time constant	6.9 sec
Short circuit time constant	1.28 sec

SPECIFIC CONSUMPTION OF MATERIALS

Copper	0.0316 kg/kVA
Steel	0.243 kg/kVA
Total	0.54 kg/kVA

MECHANICAL SPECIFICATIONS
Stresses in rotor steel
(Material - rotor steel)

Ultimate tensile strength	75 kg/mm²
Yield point	60 kg/mm²
Percentage elongation (l = 5d)	16%
Tooth stress (maximum) for n = 3000- 3600 rev/min	22/31.8 kg/mm²
Bore stress for n = 3600 rev/min	42.4 kg/mm²

Stresses in rotor copper
(Material - hardened copper)

Ultimate tensile strength	20- 30 kg/mm²
Yield point	15.20 kg/mm²
Pressure between top turns	7.7 kg/mm²
Compressive stresses in top turn of rotor	13 kg/mm²

Stresses in end bell
(Material - titanium alloy)

Ultimate tensile strength	100 kg/mm²
Yield point	98 kg/mm²
Percentage elongation	15%
Maximum stress at n = 3600 rev/min	61 kg/mm²

Critical speeds

First critical speed	1210 rev/min

Second critical speed	4080 rev/min
Maximum shaft deflection	0.732 mm
Resonant frequency of stator core	175 c/s
Resonant frequency of stator casing	73 c/s

A comparative analysis of mechanical calculations for three turbo-generators is made in Table 8.

TABLE 8

Data	Unit of measurement	Turbo-generator		
		Hydrogen cooled 100 MVA	Hydrogen cooled 150 MVA	750 MW
Dimensions of rotor				
Diameter of body	mm	1000	1075	1250
Length of body	mm	5400	6400	6500
Journal diameter	mm	400	400	500
Bearing centres	mm	8550	9700	9500
Total length of rotor . .	mm	10,505	11,770	12,000
Rotational speed				
Peripheral speed of body at $n = 3000$-3600 rev/min	m/sec	188/157	203/169	235/196
Peripheral speed of shaft journal at $n = 3600$-3000 rev/min	m/sec	75.5/63	75.5/63	95/78
Critical speeds I/II . .	rev/min	1100/3740	965/3380	1210/4080
Specifications for rotor material				
Yield point	kg/mm²	55	60	65
Ultimate tensile strength	kg/mm²	73	75	80
Elongation at $l = 5d$ . .	%	16	15	—

TABLE 8 *(continued)*

Data	Unit of measurement	Turbo-generator		
		Hydrogen cooled 100 MVA	Hydrogen cooled 150 MVA	750 MW

Stresses

Tooth stress (maximum) for $n = 3000$ rev/min	kg/mm²	19.7	20.2	22.0
Tooth stress (maximum) for $n = 3600$ rev/min	kg/mm²	28.4	29.2	31.8
Bore stress at $n = 3600$ rev/min	kg/mm²	28.5(15.8)*	32.2(17.5)	42.4 (22.5)
Factor of safety of rotor	—	∿ 1.9	∿ 2.0	∿ 1.5 (2.0)
Rotor Material	—	Steel OKhN3M OKhN4M	Steel OKhN3M OKhN4M	Rotor Steel

Dimensions of end bell

Outside diameter	mm	1065	1156	1330
Inside diameter	mm	920	994	1170
Length	mm	1150	995	705
Maximum shaft deflection .	mm	0.889	1.173	0.732

Specification for end bell material

Material	—	EI 503 steel	EI 503 steel	Titanium alloy
Yield point	kg/mm²	85	90	∿ 95
Ultimate tensile strength	kg/mm²	100	98	100-110
Elongation for $l = 5d$ . . .	%	20	20	∿ 15
Stress on end bell at $n = 3600$ rev/min	kg/mm²	51	57.1	61

* The figures in brackets refer to the mean tangential stress in the rotor body.

The stator voltage and electromagnetic loads were selected from a comparative analysis of calculated data for several different designs. The gap was selected to minimize the loss in the machine at the selected electromagnetic loads.

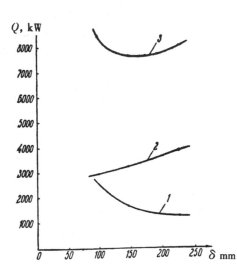

FIG. 31. Losses in a 750 MW turbo-generator as a function of gap size:
1 — stray losses;
2 — excitation loss;
3 — total loss

The proposed 750 MW turbo-generator is illustrated in Fig. 32 (sectional view). Its main design features will now be briefly considered.

(a) **Stator**. The stator is mainly of conventional design. The stator casing is made from thick (30 mm) sheet steel and is a cylinder with transverse walls open at the bottom. The outside diameter of the casing on the face is 4200 mm, the maximum possible for transport by rail. Some of the gas-coolers are placed in a special container which is transported separately and fixed to the lower part of the casing during erection. The gas-coolers in the casing are mounted horizontally in the axial direction. The container for the coolers is oval in cross section and is provided with transverse ribs to increase its strength.

The stator core is made from cold-rolled, grain-oriented electrical sheet steel with 91 packets, the maximum thickness being 60 mm owing to cooling requirements. The stator weighs about 270 metric tons ready for transport without the winding, but about 290 metric tons with the winding.

A bar-type stator winding is used with a basket-type overhang.

The bars consist of four vertical stacks of conductors 5.8 × × 274 mm². A row of internal rectangular cooling tubes is arranged vertically in the centre of the bar (see Fig. 33). The insulation is "8 mm thick" and is a form of micanite with a more stable and firmer bonding substance than bituminous varnish (a figure of 9 mm is quoted in the Table, Translator).

The electrical circuit of the winding is of conventional design with two parallel paths. The usual clamping methods are proposed. Water cooling has been adopted for the stator winding, but gas cooling for the core (hydrogen at 3 atm).

(b) **Rotor.** The rotor is a single forging. Bearing in mind the long term plans of the iron and steel industry, it is assumed that such forgings will cease to present any difficulty. At the present time such a large rotor would have to be a composite structure similar to the types of rotor produced by Brown-Boveri.

The rotor is to be machined in the usual way except for the slots for the current conductors and the water supply to the rotor winding.

The rotor winding is made from copper tube. One feature of the winding is the sealing bush for the water pipes in the overhang of each coil to supply water in parallel to all the turns of the coil (Fig. 34). This involves an alteration in coil construction since connexions must be arranged for the water on the side of the conductor when packing the winding in the slot.

It is envisaged that a titanium alloy will be used for the end

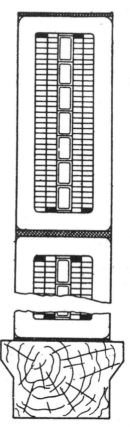

FIG. 33. Cross section of stator slot

bell. Since the modulus of elasticity of titanium is almost half that of steel, it is impossible to secure titanium support rings by shrinking. Instead it is connected to the rotor body by teeth which are milled out of the internal surface of the support ring nose and fitted in the rotor slot (Fig. 34).

The centering ring is composed of two concentric rings which are connected by an intermediate sectional ring. The internal steel ring is shrunk onto the shaft and the external ring is keyed to the end bell. The intermediate ring is so made that radial deformation of the outboard end of the shaft is not transmitted to the external ring and end bell.

The current connector has two parallel circuits. Between the slip rings and centering ring it consists of round insulated bars which are fitted in special holes. These current-conducting bars are connected to the coil by means of flexible bus bars which are placed in slots.

(c) **The end covers and bearings.** In order to reduce the overall length of the generator, the bearing pedestal and the lower half of the end cover at the exciter end is made in one piece, the pedestal resting on the foundations. The pedestal at the turbine end is integral with the turbine bearing in the usual way.

CONCLUSIONS

1. It has been established that a 750 MW turbo-generator is a practicable proposition and that its prospects are promising.

2. The increased specific loadings of the stator and rotor associated with the increased output will make it necessary to use internal liquid cooling for the windings, which in turn require parallel paths for the cooling liquid in the rotor coils in order to provide an adequate cooling system for the rotor winding.

3. The theoretical analysis of typical power progression series in section III showed that the output of generators cannot be increased appreciably by increasing specific loadings with constant rotor diameter to maintain mechanical strength and running stability since this increases costs and adversely affects

performance.

4. The analysis of stresses in rotor bodies by the theory of elastic-plastic deformation and the experience which has been gained in contempory designs indicates that the factors of safety now specified in the U.S.S.R. are unduly high and that as a result a larger diameter rotor is a practicable proposition.

5. It will no longer be possible to use steel end bells for such large rotors owing to the increased mechanical stresses which they must sustain. It will therefore be necessary to use strong lightweight titanium-type alloys which possess a greater factor of strength (i.e. a larger ratio of ultimate tensile strength to specific weight). It is also necessary to continue the search for new techniques, e.g. the development of turbo-generators without end bells.

6. From calculations and test results [16], the resonant frequency of the stator casings of very large turbo-generators tends to fall towards the frequency of the disturbing electromagnetic forces. An improvement in casing rigidity to give higher resonant frequencies entails an increase in casing size and weight. It has, however, been established that "flexible" casings can be made with resonant frequencies lower than the frequency of the disturbing force. This saves material and reduces the weight and size of the casing for the same vibration stability.

CHAPTER VI

CONCLUSION

The planned increase in unit output can only be achieved by solving the following scientific and technical problems which recent research has brought to light.

1. It is necessary to determine the optimum internal geometry of direct-cooled turbo-generators with increased specific loading by theoretical analysis and tests.

2. The minimum factor of safety and maximum possible rotor diameter for titanium-alloy end bells have to be established by tests on models and prototype machines. The properties of titanium alloys and their use for end bells need further study.

3. Research has to be undertaken to study the running stability of rotors and stators in very large turbo-generators in the light of new resilient couplings and the different mass of the various parts.

4. Further research is required into direct cooling systems in order to discover the best methods from the point of view of reliability, effectiveness and total cost.

5. The criteria of optimum excitation systems must be determined more exactly.

6. Improved mathematical methods of analysis are required. For this purpose further theoretical analysis and testing is required to study the stray losses in direct-cooled turbo-generators with increased specific loading.

7. Developmental research is required in the following directions: the use of end bell assemblies with titanium support rings, which require reliable methods of securing the support ring; rotor designs without end bells; a device for supplying the cooling liquid to the turns of the rotor winding coils in parallel; a current connector to the rotor winding which will ensure reliable

operation at high excitation currents; a reliable means of resiliently securing the stator core and so on.

8. Improved stator winding insulation is required in order to increase the rated voltage.

9. Development and utilization of physical and mathematical modelling in order to study the electromagnetic, mechanical and hydraulic phenomena of turbo-generators.

These problems relate direct to the generators, but there are also others which arise in connexion with the technical and economic efficiency of very large coal-burning power stations. In this respect the first problems are to design suitable steam turbines and to determine the scope for single-and twin-shaft sets.

Such a wide range of scientific problems can of course only be solved by the collaboration of many specialized scientific organizations.

The technical science department of the U.S.S.R. Academy of Sciences has decided in pursuance of the Academy's resolution in general assembly dated 26 May 1959 to enlist the services of the Electromechanics Institute of the U.S.S.R. Academy of Sciences, the Power Institute of the U.S.S.R. Academy of Sciences, the Metallurgy Institute of the U.S.S.R. Academy of Sciences and the Mechanics Institute of the U.S.S.R. Academy of Sciences for the solution of these problems and to request the assistance of the Central Boiler Turbine Institute, the All-Union Electromechanics Research Institute and the factories engaged in the production of large electrical machines.

GLOSSARY OF NOTATION

A_1 — specific loading of stator

A_2 — specific loading of rotor

B_δ — gap flux density

$B_{\nu c}$ — flux density on surface of the rotor due to the ν-th (n-th) harmonic of stator m.m.f.

$B_{\nu p}$ — flux density on surface of the stator due to the ν-th harmonic of rotor m.m.f.

$B_{z(0.2)}$ — flux density in the rotor teeth on no load and at rated voltage at a point 0.2 of the tooth length from the bottom of the slot

c — heat capacity of cooling medium

$d = 4S/\pi$ — equivalent hydraulic diameter of a duct

D_1 — stator bore diameter

D_2 — rotor body diameter

E'_v — e.m.f. behind Potier reactance

F_0 — no load m.m.f.

F_a — armature reaction m.m.f.

F — heat-dissipating surface of a duct

F_k — heat-dissipating surface of k-th insulation layer

Gr — Grashof number $\left(Gr = \dfrac{\beta \cdot g \cdot d^3 \cdot \Delta t_2}{(\nu')^2} \right)$

g — acceleration due to gravity

H_ν — intensity of magnetic field for the ν-th harmonic

H_j — inertia constant

Δh — pressure drop

k_c — air gap coefficient

$k_{\nu 1-2}$ — reduction factor for the flux due to the ν-th harmonic of stator m.m.f.

$k_{\nu 2-1}$ — the same, for the rotor

71

k_ν — the same for stator and rotor neglecting surface curvature

$k''_{r\nu}$ — reaction coefficient for the ν-th harmonic of the stator m.m.f.

$k'_{r\nu}$ — the same for the rotor m.m.f.

$k'_{w\nu}$ — stator winding coefficient for k ν-th harmonic

$k''_{w\nu}$ — rotor winding coefficient for the ν-th harmonic

k_i — correction coefficient for the excitation Potier diagram

k_q — the same for the rotor winding loss

l_1 — stator active length

l_2 — rotor body length

l — duct length

Nu — Nusselt number

n — r.p.m. of generator

n_n — number of bends in a duct

Pr — Prandtl number ($Pr = c\nu/\lambda$)

P_a — active power of generator

p — winding loss in one ventilation duct

p_k — heat flow across k-th insulation layer

Q_{Cu} — copper loss

Q_{Fe} — iron loss

Q_{ex} — excitation loss

$Q = vS$ — volume flow of cooling medium through one ventilation duct

Re — Reynolds number ($Re = vd/\nu'$)

R_c — mean gap radius

R_1 — stator bore radius

R_2 — rotor body radius

R_{eb} — mean radius of end bell

R_{1eb}, R_{2eb} — external and internal radii of end bell

s_1 — stator winding current density

s_2 — rotor winding current density

s_{stat} — steady state overload capability

S — cross sectional area of duct

Δt_m — maximum temperature rise of copper

Δt_1 — maximum temperature rise of cooling medium in duct

Δt_2 — temperature drop at duct surface

Δt_3 — temperature drop from the most distant conductor to the ventilation duct surface

v — velocity cooling medium in duct

x''_d — sub-transient reactance

x'_d — transient reactance

x_d — synchronous reactance

a — heat transfer coefficient

β — coefficient of volumetric expansion of cooling medium

γ — specific weight of end bell material

δ — gap length

δ_k — thickness of k-th insulation layer

Φ_1 — stator flux on no load at rated voltage

Φ'_1 — the same, but at the voltage E'_v

Φ_2 — rotor flux for rated load

Φ_{os} — total rotor leakage flux due to no load e.m.f.

Φ_{as} — total rotor leakage flux due to armature reaction m.m.f.

Φ_{sn0}, — rotor slot and air gap leakage flux respectively due to no
$\Phi_{s\delta0}$ load e.m.f.

Φ_{snk}, — the same due to armature reaction m.m.f.
$\Phi_{s\delta k}$

λ — coefficient of thermal conductivity of cooling medium

λ_k — thermal conductivity of k-th insulation layer

μ_0 — gap permeance

μ — viscosity of cooling medium

ν — order of harmonic

ν' — kinematic viscosity of cooling medium

ξ_f — coefficient of friction

ξ_r — specific loss of head due to rotation

ξ_{in} — entry loss

ξ_{out} — exit loss

π — perimeter of duct

ρ — density of cooling medium

σ — mechanical stress in rotor

σ_s — yield point

σ_B — ultimate tensile strength

$\delta k_c/\tau_c$ — ratio of gap to pole pitch

REFERENCES

1. AKSYUTIN S. A; *Prospects for the development of steam and gas turbines*, (Perspektivy razvitiya parovykh i gazovykh turbine). Mashgiz, (1957).

2. PAKSHVER V. B; *Technical and economic indices of large coal-burning power stations*, (Tekhniko-ekonomicheskiye pokazateli tepolvykh elektrostantsii bol'shoi moshchnosti). G.E.I. (1957).

3. ZHILIN V. G; The main lines of development in heat engineering 1959-1965, *Energetik*, No. 9, (1958).

4. *Power*, No. 9, p. B-6 (1957).

5. *Power*, No. 9, p. B-176 (1957).

6. Selecting the unit power of turbo-generators for large power systems. *Energokhozyaistvo za rubezhom*, No. 1, (1956).

7. *Forced hydrogen cooling of turbo-generators*, (Forsirovannoye okhlazhdeniye turbogeneratorov vodorodom). G.E.I. (1956).

8. Grenzleistungs-Turbogeneratoren, *BB Mitt.*, No. 1, (1958).

9. KILBOURNE and HOLLEY; Liquid cooling of turbine-generator armature windings, *Trans. AIEE*, III, (1956).

10. BROWNING, HOLLEY and QUINLAND; Water cooling of turbine-generator stator windings, *Trans. AIEE*, III (1958).

11. Turbo-generator with water-cooled stator windings, *The Engineer*, 14 Dec. 1956.

12. IVANOV N.P; Aspects of the design of turbo-generators with direct cooling, *Elektrichestvo*, No. 11 (1957).

13. TITOV V.V. and KOGAN Z.B; A turbo generator rotor with direct cooling, *Elektrichestvo*, No. 11 (1957).

14. YEZOVIT G.P; *Achievements in electrical machines and switchgear*, (Dostizheniya v elektromashinostroenii i apparatostroenii). TsBTI, Leningrad (1959).

15. FECHHEIMER; Liquid cooling of A.C. turbine-generators, *Trans. AIEE*, 69 (1950).

16. KOMAR Ye. G; *Aspects of turbo-generator design*, (Voprosy proektirovaniya turbogeneratorov). G.E.I. (1955).

17. *Excitation systems of large turbo-generators,* (Sistemy vozbuzh-deniya krupnykh turbogeneratorov). Teploelektroproekt report Moscow Power System, Moscow, September (1958).

18. RIKHTER; Elektrical machines, pt. II. (Elektricheskiye mashiny, ch. II). *United Scientific and Technical Press* (1936).

19. POSTNIKOV I. M; *The design of electrical machines,* (Proektirovanie elektricheskikh mashin). Gostekhizdat, Ukr. SSR, Kiev (1952.

20. POSTNIKOV I.M; Eddy currents in synchronous and asynchronous machines, *Elektrichestvo,* No. 10 (1958).

21. KASHARSKII E'.G; In book: Achievements in electrical machines and switchgear, (Dostizheniya v elektromashinostroenii i apparatostroenii). TsBTI, Leningrad (1959).

22. STAATS; Eddy currents in end windings. *El. Eng.,* 76, No. 7 (1957).

23. WINCHESTER; Stray losses in the armature end iron of large turbine generators, *Trans. AIEE,* June (1957).

24. MOCHEL *et al* Large rotor forgings for turbines and generators, *Trans. ASME,* 78, No. 7, (1956).

25. KHARMS; Problems of mechanical strength of turbo-generators of maximum power, In book: Modern synchronous generators, (Sovremennyye sinkhronnyye generatory). (1958).

26. KACHANOV L.M; *Fundamentals of the theory of plasticity,* (Osnovy teorii plastichnosti), Gostekhizdat, (1956).

27. *The theory of plasticity,* (Teoriya plastichnosti). A collection of articles edited by Yu.N. Rabotnov (1948).

28. ALEKSEYEV A.E., URUSOV I.D. and ANEMPODISTOV V.P.; Turbo generator rotor. Patent dated 15 May 1959.

29. HARMS; *Wasserstoffgekühlte Generatoren grosser Leistung,* ETZ-A, No. 3 (1957).

30. SAKHAROV I.E. and TER-MIKAELYAN T.M.; *A computer study of the critical speeds of a rotor on resilient-solid supports,* (Raschet na elektronnoi schetnoi mashine kriticheskikh skorostei rotora na uprugo-massivnykh oporakh). All-Union Electrical Engineering Institute, No. 5 (1957).

31. BELNO *et al.; BB Mitt.,* Nos. 4 and 5 (1958).

32. MIKHEYEV M.A.; *Fundamentals of heat transfer,* (Osnovy teorii teploobmena). G.E.I., (1949).

33. KUTATELADZE S.S.; *Fundamentals of the theory of heat exchange,* (Osnovy teorii teploobmena). Mashgiz (1957).

34. FRANKL N.Z.; *Hydraulics,* GEI, 1956.

35. URUSOV I.D.; In book: The cooling of turbo and hydro-electric generators, (Okhlazhdeniye turbo-i gidrogeneratorov). Moscow (1959).

36. KASHARSKII E'.G. and SUKHANOV L.A. ; *Inter-college conference on the use of physical and mathematical modelling.* Report F-07, Moscow (1959).

37. ANEMPODISTOV V.P. and ANEMPODISTOVA N.N. ; *Inter-college conference on the use of physical and mathematical modelling.* Report F-12, Moscow (1959).

38. URUSOV I.D. and PODREZ V.M. ; *Physical modelling of the rigidity and vibrostability of an electrical machine's stator shell, Electric Technology,* U.S.S.R. Vol. 4, Pergamon Press (1959). (Translation from *Elektrichestvo* No. 10, 1959).